Bananas & Cream

**Fifty Fantastically Funny Limericks
(with some tips for writing your own)**

DAVID SMITH
(aka Ivor Folio)

Illustrated by Pam Flitt

DEDICATION

This collection is dedicated to the children who have attended Bananas & Cream workshops and for those yet to come.

It is also dedicated to my son, Ben, and to the Harvey family, for whom many of the earliest poems in this collection were written.

Thanks too to Peppy Scott, my favourite partner in rhyme and the Pam to my Ivor, for the wonderful illustrations.

CONTENTS

FIRST STEPS

I have been reciting limericks for as long as I can remember and writing them since I first picked up a pencil and learned my ABCs. I must have made up thousands over the years, mostly written in birthday cards or on scraps of paper as disposable poems for immediate use. Others never even made it that far; kept in my head and recited only once or twice before melting away like snowflakes landing on a warm nose.

The poems in this collection were written for children, some for specific children and some for the groups of children who have attended Bananas and Cream workshops. They can be enjoyed just for fun, or, for those interested in writing their own limericks, as examples to learn from. I suggest a bit of both.

So what's the connection between limericks and "Bananas and Cream", I hear you ask? Well, the simple answer is rhythm. Limericks – all poetry in fact, but especially verse and other rhymed forms – are written to rhythms and beats. These beats, also known as "feet" or "metre", are more fully explained at the back of the book, where you'll find them listed under their posh Latin names. For now, though, we're going to look at just two of them, and we're going to call them "Banana" (three beats: ba-na-na) and "and cream" (two beats: and-cream).

With variations of these two beats and some end rhymes you can write limericks till the cows come home. You need thirteen bananas in total, or, if you prefer, you can make equally delicious limericks with fewer bananas and extra lashings of lovely cream. The next couple of pages will show you how, and then we'll get to the limericks themselves.

THIRTEEN BANANAS (and some cream)

Banana banana banana
Banana banana banana
Banana banana
Banana banana
Banana banana banana

If you read the above with a short pause at the end of each line you will have found the limerick rhythm. If thirteen bananas seems heavy going – and it usually does! – you can add some cream. Let's add some at the end of each line now and see what happens:

Banana banana and cream
Banana banana and cream
Banana and cream
Banana and cream
Banana banana and cream.

Too much cream? Well how about:

Banana banana and cream
Banana banana and cream
Banana banana
Banana banana
Banana banana and cream?

OR:

Banana banana banana
Banana banana and cream
And cream and banana
And cream and banana
And cream and banana and cream!
☐
There are other combinations too and other beats that can

be used instead of bananas and cream, but we'll stick with what we've got for now. We'll look instead at other ingredients that are found in (most) limericks, the first one being…

END RHYME

End rhymes are exactly what they sound like: rhyming words found at the ends of lines of poetry. Simple, isn't it! Limericks usually have two sets of rhymes, which we will call rhyme "A" and rhyme "B". The "A" rhymes appear at the ends of the longer lines, 1, 2 and 5 and the "B" rhymes are found on the shorter lines, 3 and 4. If we replace the bananas on the ends of each line with end rhymes we get something like this:

Banana banana and jelly
banana banana and telly
Banana and pickle
banana and tickle
banana banana and smelly

NAMES AND PLACES (where it all begins)

Traditionally limerick poems tell stories, usually funny and often quite rude (but not too rude, please!). The first line generally introduces the reader to the character the story is about, sometimes by name and sometimes by where they live. Like this: *I know of a Scotsman called Willy…*

The first line usually gives us the "A" rhyme for the rest of the poem.

We'll look at some variations to these rules later in the book, but for now we know more than enough to make a start. Let's finish Willy's story, then, and feel free to count the bananas (and creamy dollops) as you're reading…

CHILLY WILLY

I know of a Scotsman called Willy

Whose kilt is so thin he gets chilly

When he hikes on the heath

With pyjamas beneath

He's warm but he looks rather silly

***

A SEEDY TALE

There was a young lady from Leeds

Who swallowed a packet of seeds

A single red rose

Grew out of her nose

And her lugholes were covered in weeds

***

SCRUFFY JADE

A scruffy young lady called Jade

Wore jumpers her grandmother made

The sleeves were too long

And the body shape wrong

While the necks were all tatty and frayed

***

BO PEEP

There was a young girl called Bo Peep

Who struggled to get any sleep

Her doctor suggested

At night when she rested

She might want to try counting sheep

***

'I suppose you've tried the obvious?'

(Cartoon originally printed in *Times of Tunbridge Wells*)

ALEX THE BOXER

Young Alex's boxing disaster

Began when a keen P.E. master

Said 'swing at this ball

That I've hung on the wall'

Now A's to his elbow in plaster

***

LUKE THE CHEF

An aspiring young gourmet called Luke

Was invited to cook for a Duke

His main course was nice:

Chicken curry and rice

But his cheesecake made everyone puke

***

THE FOOL IN THE POOL

There's a girl in my swim class at school

Who peed as we splashed in the pool

They easily caught her –

There's dye in the water

That changes the colour, the fool!

***

PIERRE CUTS

A Parisian coiffeur named Pierre

Offers cuts of distinction and flair

From a chic Marcel Wave

To a cheap buzz-cut shave

Or the classic Canard's Derrière

***

A BIRD, A CAT AND A WORM

A worm in the garden's a treat

For a bird who wants something to eat

But he'd best stay aware

Of the cat who lives there

Who would breakfast on fresh shredded tweet

***

CHEEKY BEN

There was a young fellow named Ben

Who was cheeky just now and again

And again, and again

And again, and again

And again, and again, and again...

***

WHERE'S JILL?

I know of a lady called Jill

Who planned a day's outing in Rhyl

At Crewe intersection

She lost her direction

And wound up in deepest Brazil

***

POOR PIES

I know of a baker in Fakenham

Whose pies have no kidney or steak in 'em

Just gravy and air,

The occasional hair

I can't see the point in him making 'em

***

LAMORNA LORNA

I knew a young lady called Lorna

Who went on her hols to Lamorna

She loved the sea breeze

And the views and cream teas

And the interesting flora and fauna

***

A GOOD ~~WATCHDOG~~ CLOCK DOG

I heard there's a dog in Chihuahua

Who barks every hour on the hour

They recently taught her

To yelp every quarter

And built her her very own tower

***

CRAZY GOLF

I know of a famed golfer's son

Much maligned as a figure of fun

His worst exhibition

In one competition –

A hole in one hundred and one!

***

TUNBRIDGE WELLS TALES (I)

There once was a Tunbridge Wells gent

Who farted wherever he went

So if you go down

To that smelly old town

You'll probably pick up his scent!

***

Ivor Folio is blessed with the good fortune to live in Royal Tunbridge Wells, a beautiful Kentish spa town famed for the health-giving qualities of its natural springs. This provides much inspiration for Ivor's poetry.

TUNBRIDGE WELLS TALES (II)

A Tunbridge Wells mum of renown

Would dress every day as a clown

This may seem to you

Quite an odd thing to do

But it made her the talk of the town

***

TUNBRIDGE WELLS TALES (III)

I know of a man and his daughter

Who swallowed some Tunbridge Wells water

It drove them quite mad

This poor girl and her dad:

I think I'll just stick to the porter*

***

* Porter is a delicious dark BEER enjoyed by real ale enthusiasts like Ivor and Pam. Younger visitors to the town would perhaps find lemonade more to their liking.

SAM AND ELLA

A hopeless young lady named Ella

Tried cooking some fish for her fella

Her efforts, I fear,

Gave the lad diarrhoea

Diagnosis – severe salmonella

***

CREEPY- CRAWLY / CRAWLY-CREEPY

There once was an earwig from Chorley

Who crept when he should have been crawly

This haughty display

Drew a blackbird his way

There's a moral in this, reader, surely?

***

EDWARD LEAR

A limerick writer named Lear

Wrote limericks irksome and drear

For the last line of verse

Would be much like the first

That tiresome writer named Lear

***

If not the inventor of the limerick Edward Lear is certainly the man responsible for popularising the form. And yes, he did have the irksome habit of using a close variation of the first line as the last!

THE MULDOON IN THE MOON

I know a young man named Muldoon

Whose dream is to walk on the moon

He set off last night

On a dirty great kite

And hopes to be landing there soon

***

BANANAS

While travelling in the Bahamas

I ate my own weight in bananas

With all that potassium

My guts were all gassium:

I ruined my favourite pyjamas

***

PAM THE POET

There was a young poet called Pam

Who entered a poetry slam

When asked, 'Do you rhoime?'

She replied, 'All the toime,

'An' oi'm good at the rhoimin', oi am.'

***

This limerick is a small homage to Pam Ayres (a Flitt & Folio favourite). Though less apparent now, her strong regional accent was a feature of her early performance persona.

.

GREEN EGGS

There once was a vintner named Beggs

Who was famed for the wine in his kegs

It was bitter and tart

And it made people fart

But was perfect for pickling eggs

***

MIKE'S PIKE

I know of an angler called Mike

Who landed the world's biggest pike

Then spotting odd scales,

Four legs and a tail,

He quickly escaped on his bike!

***

SPOT THE DIFFERENCE

PIKE

FINS (NO LEGS)

ALLIGATOR

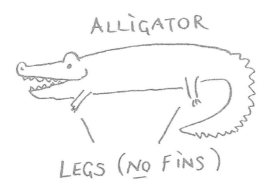

LEGS (NO FINS)

FRANK

In the queue outside Lloyd's I met Frank

Whose mask was all tatty and rank

When I said that no way

Would it keep germs at bay

He said, 'So? I'm just robbing the bank!'

***

This limerick is one of several written during lockdown for Penshurst Poetry Festival. The rest of the collection – including the prize-winner – are not really suitable for Bananas & Cream!

ALONG CAME A SPIDER…

There's a spider that lives in the Wirral

So big it could swallow a squirrel

So if you're a squirrel

Who lives in the Wirral

Ignore this advice at your pirral

***

A limerick penned on learning that the Wirral in Merseyside is home to the largest spiders in Northern Europe…

REBECCA'S BREAKFAST

A greedy young lady named Becky

Tried eating a pig for her brekky

A trotter's what got her

Though smothered in butter

It still wouldn't slip down her necky

***

YVETTE THE PO-ET

I know of a poet, Yvette,

Who most of the time will forget

When writing a rhyme

To supply a last line

***

GREEDY GANNET JANET

A greedy young lady named Janet

Would gobble down food like a gannet

Employed as a teen

Packing sprats and sardine

She would eat it before they could can it

***

BRAINY JAMIE

There's a boy in my classroom called James

Who's useless at PE and games

But he's really quite bright

And the teachers delight

In his love of facts, figures and names

***

FIDGETY BRIDGET

A fussy young lady called Bridget

Would wiggle and squiggle and fidget

Her Mum would despair,

Waving fists in the air

Crying, 'Bridget, you fidget, *what is it?*'

***

RUDE JAKE

A very rude fellow, is Jake

Who's renowned for the smells he can make

While the teachers turn puce

When he's letting one loose

His mates get a laugh during break

***

UNFAIR DISMISSAL?

There's a sad cross-eyed teacher in Seoul

Who's faced with a life on the dole

Though her work is admired

She's invariably fired

When pupils run out of control

***

SWEATY BETTY

I know a young lady called Betty

Who ate a great plate of spaghetti

That night, in her bed,

Betty groaned, overfed,

Feeling bloaty and bilious and sweaty

***

DETERMINED DOMINIC

A resourceful wee toddler called Domi

Went walking one day with his Mummy

When his legs got too weak

Did he cry? Not a squeak!

He just slithered along on his tummy!

***

THE LITTLE GENT IN VELVET

An industrious fellow, the mole

As he tunnels through meadow and knoll

He looks really cute

In his black velvet suit

But he's more of a pest on the (w)hole

***

THROWAWAY LINES

A poet from downtown Bombay

Wrote limericks every day

While most were stupendous

Amazing, tremendous

The last lines were often horrendous

***

RED ~~LETTER~~ SETTER DAY

A clever but naughty red setter

Would chase the poor post girl and get her

"Why clever?" You say,

"Dogs do that every day"

Yes, but not on a souped-up Lambretta

***

MEG'S LEGS

I know a young lady called Megs

Who's sadly allergic to eggs

Whenever this girl has been

Close to some albumin

Rashes appear on her legs

***

ROSE'S NOSE

I know a young lady called Rose

Who's always unpacking her nose

She'll pick it, then lick it,

Then roll it and flick it

And nobody knows where it goes!

***

Lines three and four, of course, are a playground refrain that was probably being sung back in Edward Lear's day. Something old and something new: what a lovely combination!

MESSING ABOUT ON THE RIVER

I know a canoeist called Owen

Who's useless in water that's flowing

He fights with the tides

While they jeer from all sides

'Hey Owen, you coming or going!?'

***

A FOOLISH YOUNG MAN FROM TIBET

A foolish young man from Tibet

Once wrestled a bear for a bet

They've found enough limbs

To identify him

But the head hasn't turned up as yet

***

THE RAIN ~~IN SPAIN~~ ON WAYNE

A bald-headed hiker called Wayne

Once set out to hike across Spain

But cranial pain

From the rain on the plain

Had him crying, *'No, never again!'*

***

WRIGGLY NELLY

I met a cute earthworm called Nelly

Who wriggled along on her belly

I thought she looked bored

So I took her indoors

To watch Dr Who on the telly

***

This limerick is based on an old poem by Spike Milligan. The illustration is based on an old episode of Dr Who.

A SNOTTY PROBLEM

A clumsy young fellow called Scott

Spilled pepper from out of the pot

He sneezed for an hour

Creating a shower

That peppered his dinner with snot

***

UNCLEAN DEAN

A mucky young fellow called Dean

Shakes hands when his hands are not clean

Don't offer to shake it,

If offered, don't take it,

You never know where it has been

***

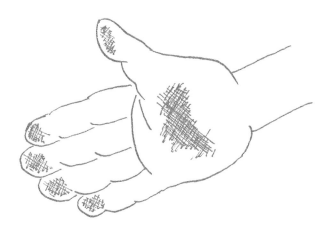

A SPIRITED PERFORMANCE

I met a clairvoyant called Fred

Who claims he can talk to the dead

We found it so funny

When he spoke to Granny –

She's currently cruising the Med!

***

JESS THE POETESS

There was a young poet called Jess

Whose poems were rhymed (more or less)

Her tutor's advice

Was to 'edit them thrice'

But Jess lacked the patience, I guess

***

It seems only fitting that we should finish this selection of limericks with a pair of poems about poets. While the lady above clearly struggled with the form, a turn of the page will reveal a young lady who made it her own...

THE YOUNG LADY FROM WORKSOP

There was a young lady from Worksop

Who went on a limerick workshop

She now writes collections

And fills several sections

Of shelving in Waterstone's bookshop

***

LOTS O' LIMERICKS
LIMERICKS!
LIMERICKS GALORE!
THE BEST LIMERICKS
LOVELY LIMERICKS!
BUMPER BOOK OF LIMERICKS
MORE LIMERICKS

LIMERICKS

LIMERICKS FOR YOU!
EVERYDAY LIMERICKS!
WE LOVE LIMERICKS
A LIMERICK A DAY
LIMERICKS!
THE BIG BOOK OF LIMERICKS
HERE COME LIMERICKS!
LIMERICKS!
HERE COME THE LIMERICKS

LIMERICKS

A LOAD OF LIMERICKS
LIMERICKS
LIMERICKS LIMERICKS LIMERICKS
A COLLECTION OF LIMERICKS
MY FAVOURITE LIMERICKS
LIMERICKS FOR ALL THE FAMILY
NAUGHTY LIMERICKS
THE WORLD'S FUNNIEST LIMERICKS

LIMERICKS

BACK WORDS

As I mentioned in the introduction, many of the poems in this book are used in the "Bananas & Cream" writing workshop, which covers limericks and many other popular poetry forms. Generating ideas is a key element of the workshops, and I have listed below some useful tips and tricks to get you started.

Happy Accidents: Some of the best ideas come from happy accidents. You might be talking to someone and two rhyming words crash together in a delightfully pleasing "You're a poet and you don't know it" kind of way. Commit them to memory or write them down and you're almost halfway to a limerick. Happy accidents are great, but not very reliable. When you're up against the clock you might have to be a little bit more creative…

Word Lists: Think of a name or place. Then write down words that rhyme. Once you've got lines 1, 2 and 5, lines 3 and 4 should be easy to fill, and all you need to do then is join the dots. There are all kinds of resources online and in books that can help you find rhyming words if you are stuck. Two of my online favourites are

www.rhymezone.com and www.wordhippo.com.

You can find other helpful writing tools there too.

To find place names, why not stick pins in a map? Online search engines will give you access to a whole planet's worth of place names, or you could even write about someone (or some*thing*) living on Mars or Venus. The world and beyond is your oyster (as are the oyster beds beneath the sea).

Life: People you know and the places you go provide great material for poems and rhymes:

- Mum: glum, hum, rum...(and bum, of course).
- Dad: sad, glad, bad...(and mad, of course).

As well as providing material for poems these people may also be your audience, and who doesn't love being the centre of attention?

Other Poems: I've written lots of new poems that are variations on old poems – my own and other people's. This isn't 'copying' if you change the form, it's wordplay! Remember to give credit to the original, though, as that makes it even more fun and shows how well-read you are.
The Wriggly Nelly poem on page 94 is a good example of this, being based on a Spike Milligan poem I first read in school.

Jokes: Old jokes can take on a new lease of life if drafted as poems. Again, it's not cheating, just wordplay. You can find several examples in this book, including the Naughty Red Setter poem on page 82.

The Media: Newsworthy events are happening all around us all of the time, and many make really good – sometimes prize-winning (smug grin) – limericks. You might find big topics like lockdown or global warming on national news, but there's equally good material to be found about cats stuck up trees or old ladies getting stuck in lavatories (oh, dear!) in local newspapers.

Animals: I write many poems about animals, as the two previous examples show. I don't have a pet, but if you do why not try writing a limerick about them? If not, write about somebody else's pet or maybe a wild animal or animals in the zoo. A neighbour of mine has a Chihuahua that barks constantly. I think it's obvious where the poem on page 30 came from!

Books, Film and TV: If you're a reader, film-goer or TV-watcher you have a wealth of inspiration at your fingertips. From Harry Potter through to EastEnders you'll find all kinds of interesting characters and situations to write about. My Wriggly Nelly poem mentions Dr Who as well as Spike Milligan, so that's two references in one limerick!

As you can see, there are all kinds of places for finding ideas or for mining for rhyme. The list above is far from complete, but should give you plenty to work with. My biggest tip would be to keep your eyes and ears open – a walk in a park or the countryside can be FILLED with inspiration (think of Wordsworth and his daffodils!). In fact, all five senses should be kept finely tuned (the *feel* of sand squishing between your toes, the *smell* of a cow pat, the *taste* of bananas and cream...) because ideas are all around us just waiting to be discovered. If we are open to ideas and welcome them in the limericks almost write themselves. That's why it's called word*play* and not word*work!*

***

And Finally: At the beginning of the book I mentioned beats, metre and rhythm. While Bananas & Cream are my personal favourites for writing limericks (and extremely memorable!) there are many other beats in poetry. Some fit limericks very well while others are less useful, but it's worth going over the most common ones in either case...

METRICAL FEET

Metre is the building block for almost all forms of poetry, providing the rhythm on which the poem is built and the "feet" on which it stands. The most common "feet" in limericks are called the anapaest and the iamb (I told you there would be some Latin!), though for Bananas & Cream we *technically* use iambs and amphibrachs, because we couldn't find a three-syllable fruit to go with our cream in our list of anapaests. Besides, amphibrachs and anapaests are almost identical anyway. For the record, "banana" is an Amphibrach, while "and" and "cream" combined add up to a single iamb

Oh. **DON'T PANIC!** We're not expecting you to remember these big Latin names, we're just giving them to you for good measure. In the simplest terms, metrical feet are defined by the way the syllables in words or groups of words are *stressed* in natural speech. Below is a list of the most commonly used metrical feet in English verse, and we have indicated the stressed (or "long") syllables in italics…

Iamb (pronounced I Am): Shakespeare's favourite by a mile! The Iamb has two syllables and the stress is on the second syllable "Across" A*cross*.

Trochee (pronounced Tro-Key, the "Tro" rhyming with "throw"): Reverse the iamb and you have a trochee. "Actor" *Act*or.

Anapaest (pronounced An-A-Peest): Three syllables, short, short, long. "Disagreed" Disa*greed*.

Dactyl (pronounced Dack-Till): Reverse the anapaest and you have a dactyl. Long, short, short. "Africa" *A*frica

Spondee (pronounced Spon-Dee): Two syllables, both stressed. "Aardvark" *Aardvark* (included because it's such a lovely word, but a double word combination like "P*ea* S*oup*" might be a clearer example).

Amphibrach (pronounced Am-Fi-Brack): The bananas in bananas & cream. Three syllables, short, long, short. "Banana" Ba*na*na.

In addition to the above there are several metrical feet with four syllables, but that's probably going too far for a book about limericks! All that really matters is that the words you've chosen fit the rhythm, whether based around the banana and amphibrach model or the "skippier" anapaest should you find my suggestion disagreeable.

Disagree, disagree, disagree

I assure you it won't bother me

Whichever's for you

May your rhythm ring true:

It's all in the metre, you see!

***

ABOUT THE AUTHORS

David Smith is a Kentish lad born and bred. As two thirds of the Gluten-free Trio he and regular co-conspirator Peppy Scott write and perform spoken word, comedy and song at venues and events around Kent and Sussex and beyond. Their "Voices" open mic evenings and variety shows, which they host as Pam Flitt and Ivor Folio, have graced many local stages, as well as encompassing radio and online broadcast.

As 2Fs Design they create everything from greeting cards to bespoke illustration and poetry for individual and corporate clients, as well as offering editorial services and content.

This collection features limericks written for their Keystage 2 writing workshop "Bananas & Cream", covering various forms of humorous verse.

Illustrations are by Peppy, who is resident cartoonist for *The Times of Tunbridge Wells.*

Find us for performance at https://voicestw.com or for all other services at https://2fsdesign.com

Printed in Great Britain
by Amazon

65314583R00068